555
Sticker Fun
Vehicles

Sandy Creek
NEW YORK

An Imprint of Sterling Publishing
1166 Avenue of the Americas
New York, NY 10036

ISBN 978-1-4351-5463-6
Manufactured in Hangzhou, China
Lot #:
6 8 10 9 7
10/16
www.sterlingpublishing.com

Busy town

Today, the town is so busy that there is gridlock—nothing is moving! Use stickers to fill the streets with vehicles of all shapes and sizes.

At the airport

It is summer, so the airport is extra busy with planes landing and taking off. Add plane stickers in the sky and on the runway, then add some other vehicles that do special jobs at an airport.

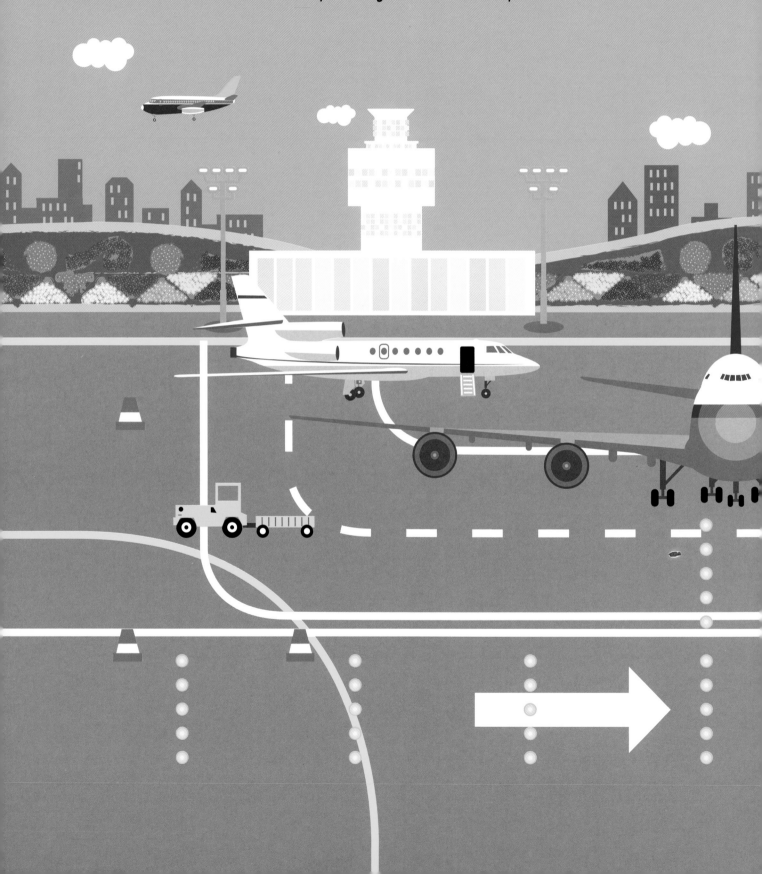

Building site

There is a lot of digging, lifting and loading to do at the building site.
Fill the scene with vehicles that are made especially to do this heavy work.

On the farm

Down on the farm, the wheat needs cutting, the field needs plowing, the cows need milking and the horses need feeding. Use stickers to complete the scene with vehicles that are designed for these jobs.

At the bus station

There is always lots to see at the bus station. Use stickers to fill it with buses and coaches of all shapes and sizes, ready to begin their journeys.

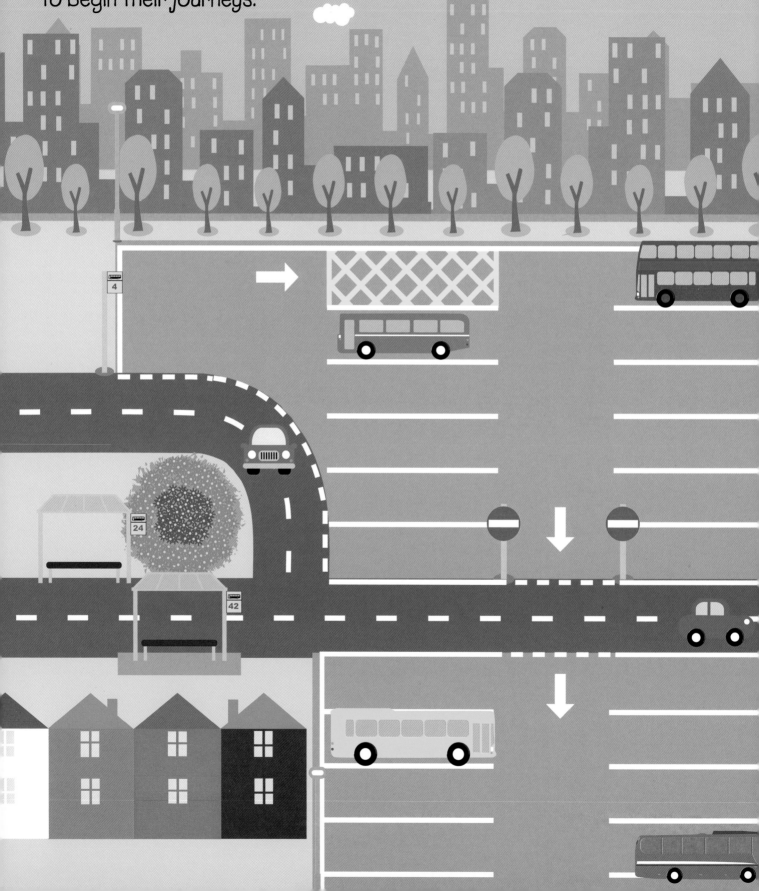

In the harbor

The harbor is a safe place for boats as it is sheltered from stormy seas.
Fill it with stickers of different boats that come and go each day.

Emergency!

Oh dear! The truck has come off the road and tipped its load.
Fill the scene with emergency vehicles to clear the logs up quickly
and safely.

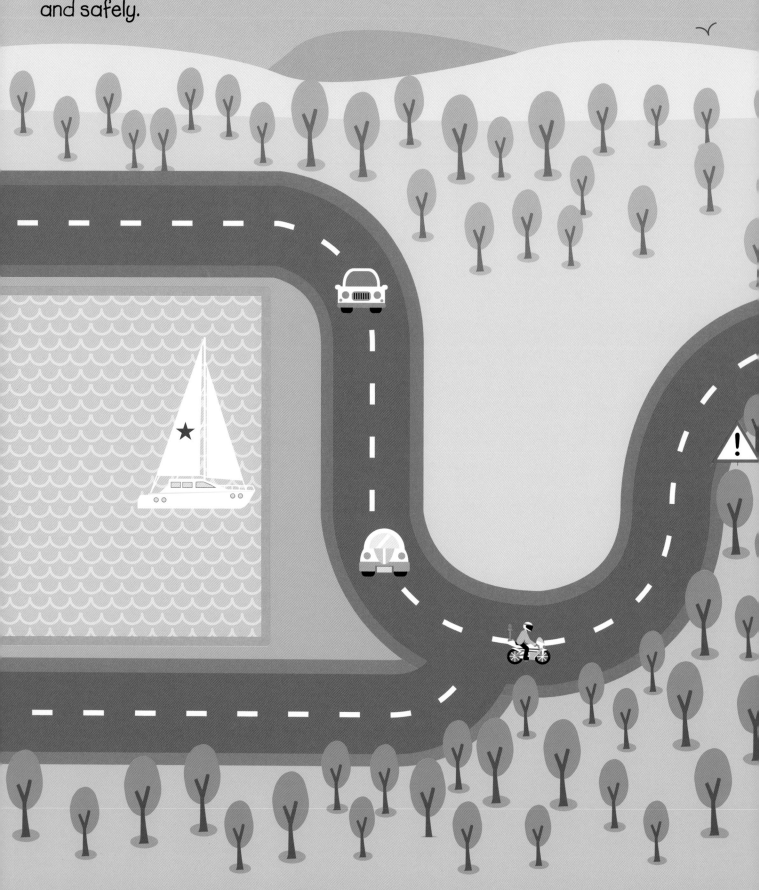

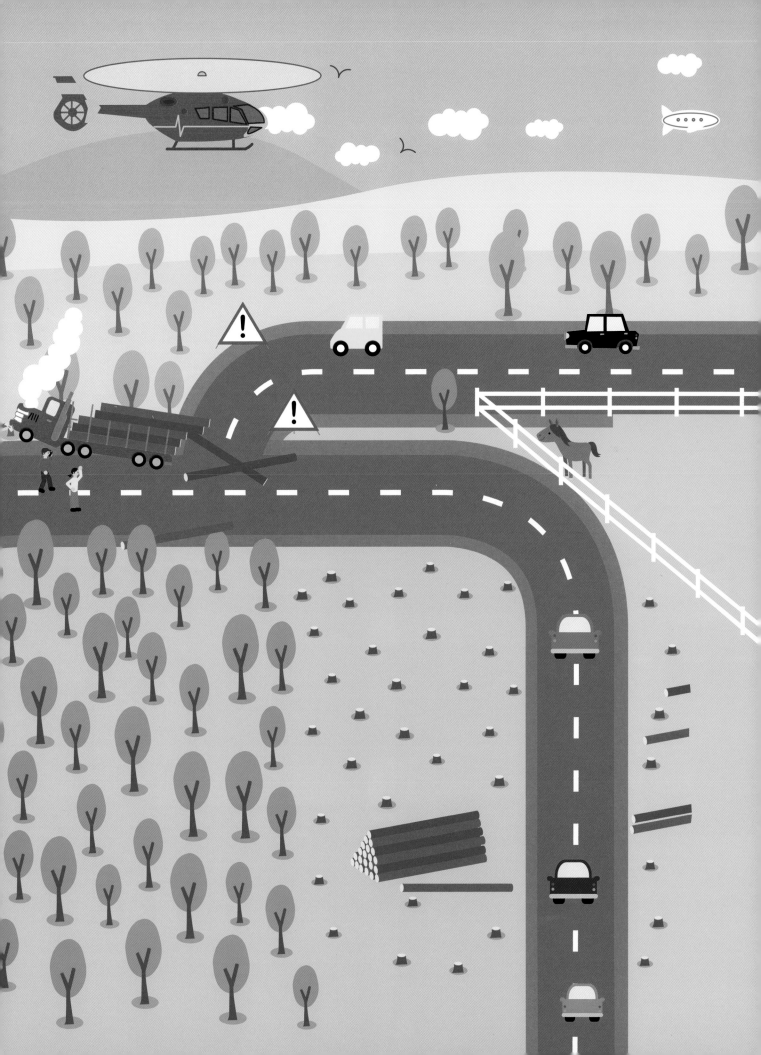

A day at the docks

At the docks, cargo ships are loaded and unloaded. Fill the scene with ships being loaded and boats in the water. Add vehicles doing jobs on the dockside.

On the campsite

It is a hot summer's day and everyone wants to go camping.
Complete the busy campsite scene with stickers of motor homes,
camper vans, tents, cars and trucks.

At the car dealership

There is plenty to do at the dealership today. Fill the scene with stickers of shiny new cars waiting to be sold and vehicles waiting to be fixed.

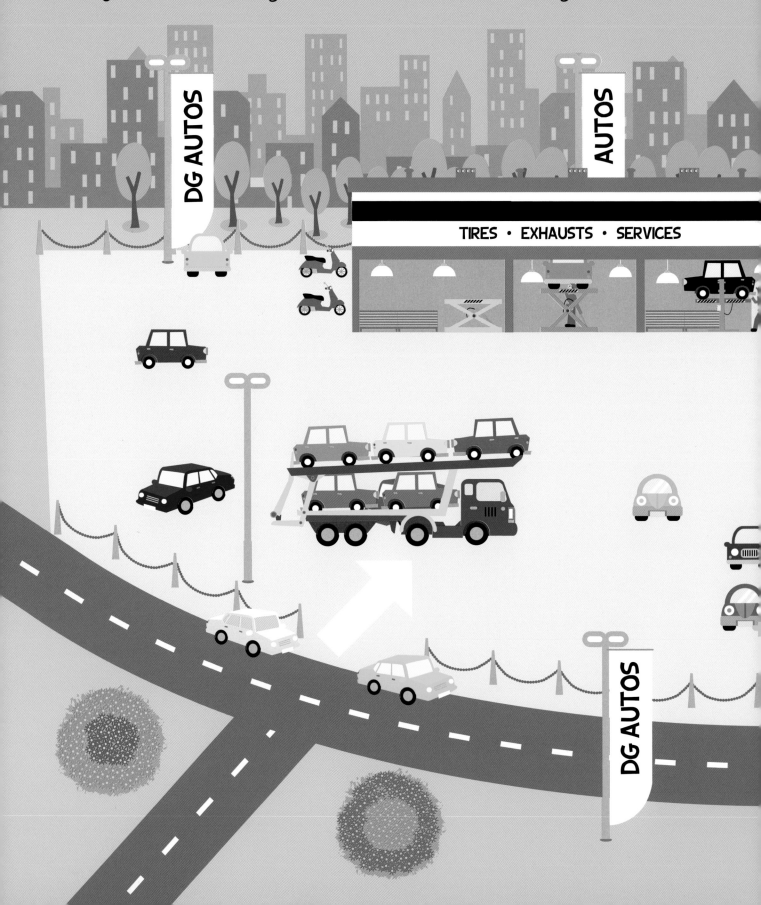

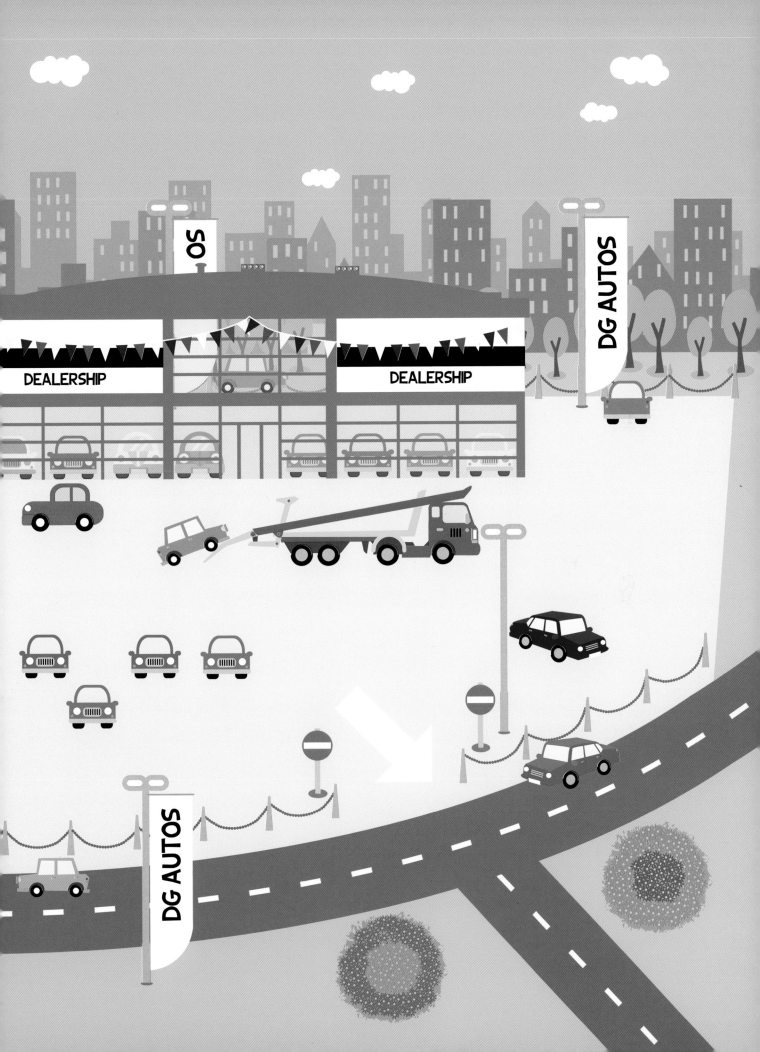

All aboard the train!

This train station is a busy, bustling place. Fill the scene with trains arriving at the platforms and vehicles that clean and carry all day.

4x4 fun

It is the day of a big 4x4 rally and everyone is ready for fun.
Fill the scene with big, tough vehicles competing in the mud.

Setting sail

It is a sunny, breezy day—perfect for a boat race. Fill the sea with sailing boats of all shapes and sizes, speeding through the waves.

Balloon flight

Today, the birds will have company high in the sky. Fill the sky with colorful hot-air balloons to bring the scene to life.

Speedy supercars

At the racetrack, everyone is very excited. The race is underway!
Fill the scene with speedy supercar stickers racing toward the finish line.

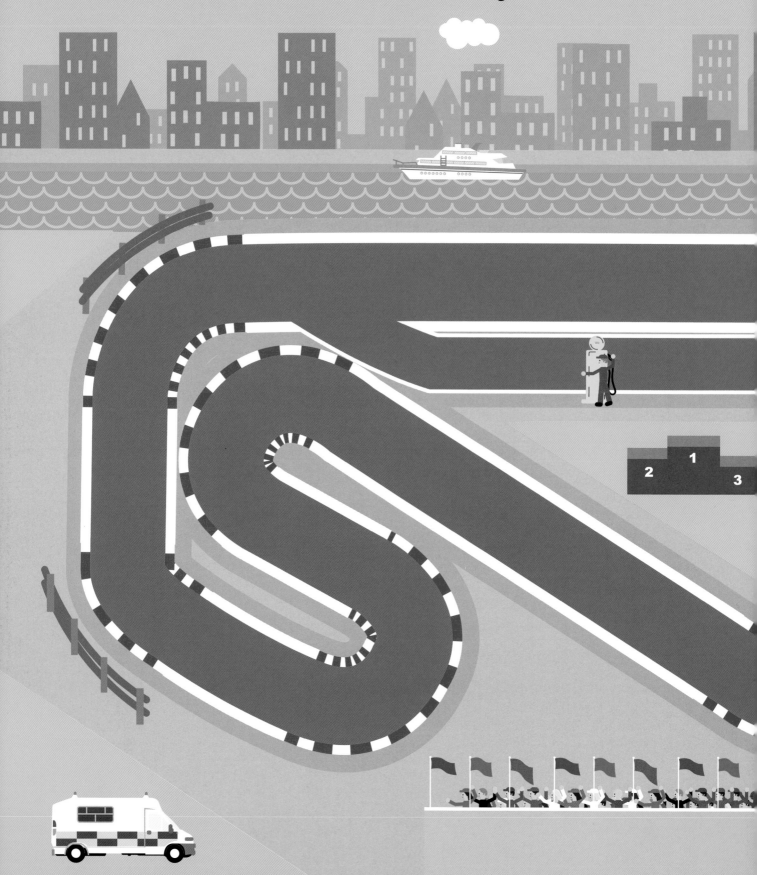

At the freight yard

The locomotives at the freight yard pull heavy loads along the tracks. Fill the scene with stickers of locomotives, wagons and cranes going about their important work.

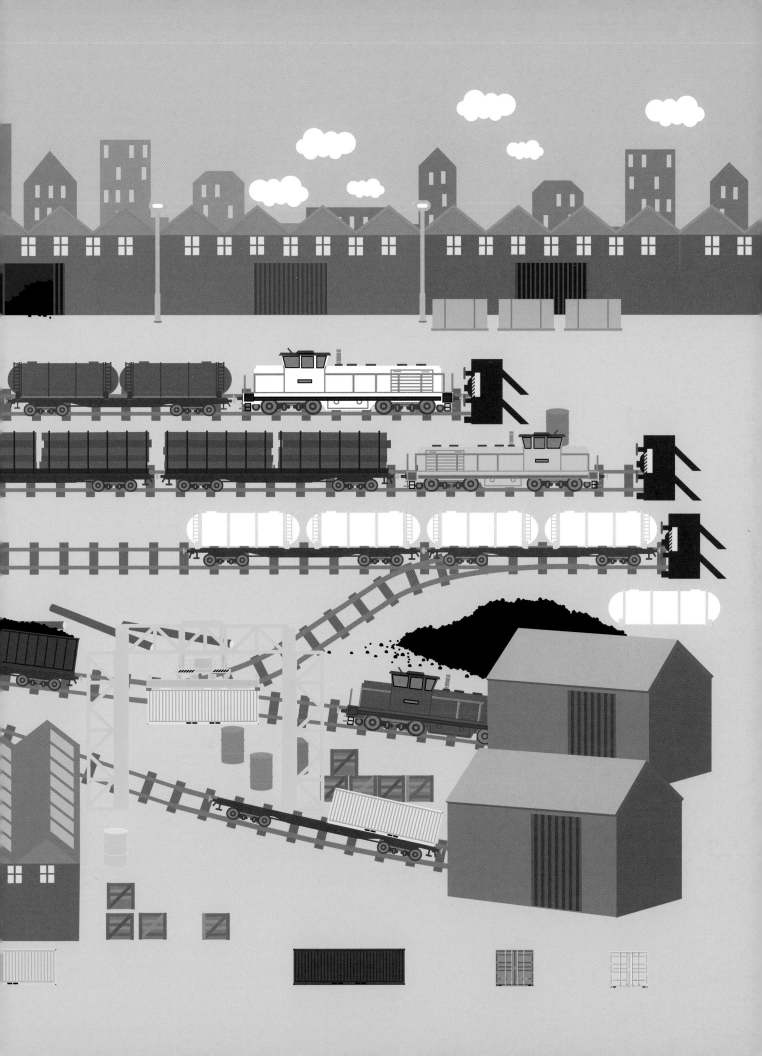

Motorbike fun day

Every year, motorbikes gather at the seaside for a fun day out.
Fill the roads at the seafront with motorbikes large and small.

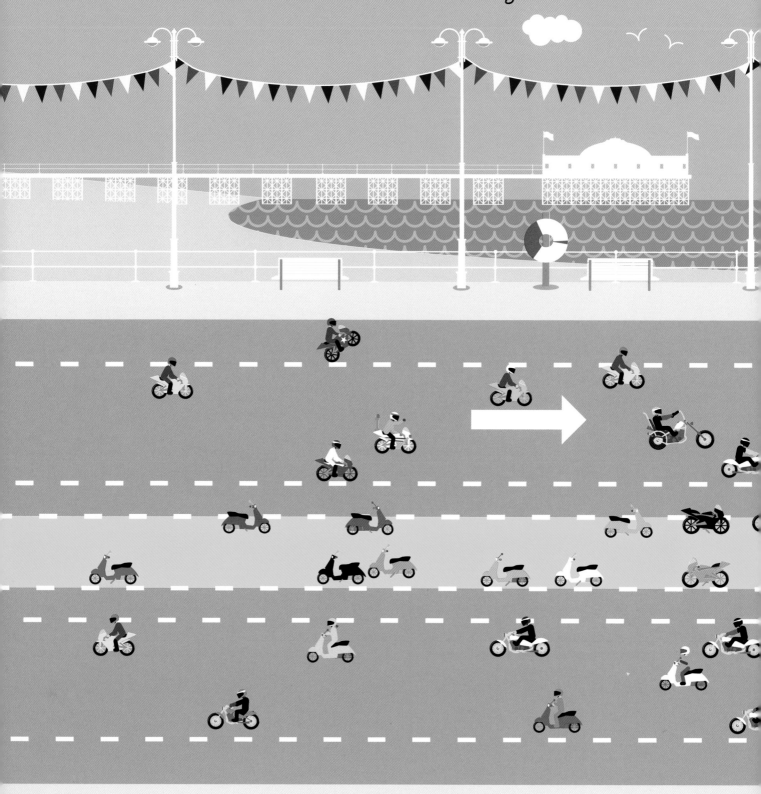

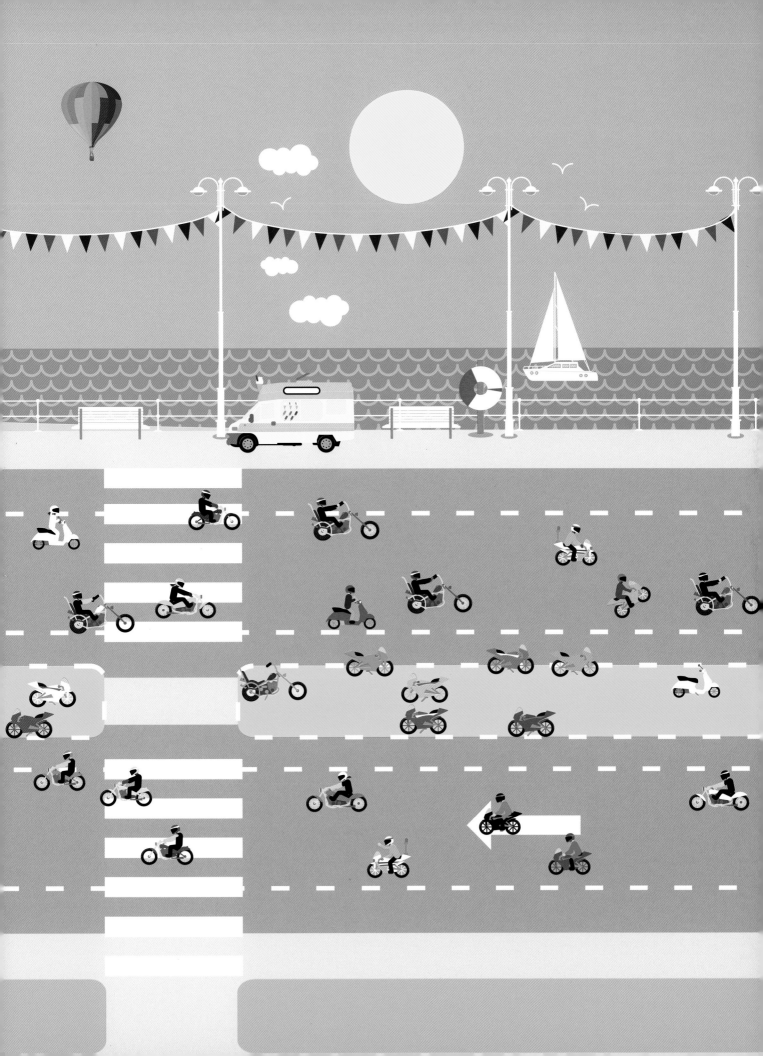

Vintage cars

There is a display of vintage cars at the park. Fill the scene with stickers of vehicles from days gone by.

Space adventure

Specially-designed vehicles travel into space to work. Fill the scene with rockets and spacecraft high above Earth.

Muscle car madness

At the stadium, the engines growl and roar.
Fill the track with weird and wonderful
muscle cars racing for
the ultimate prize.

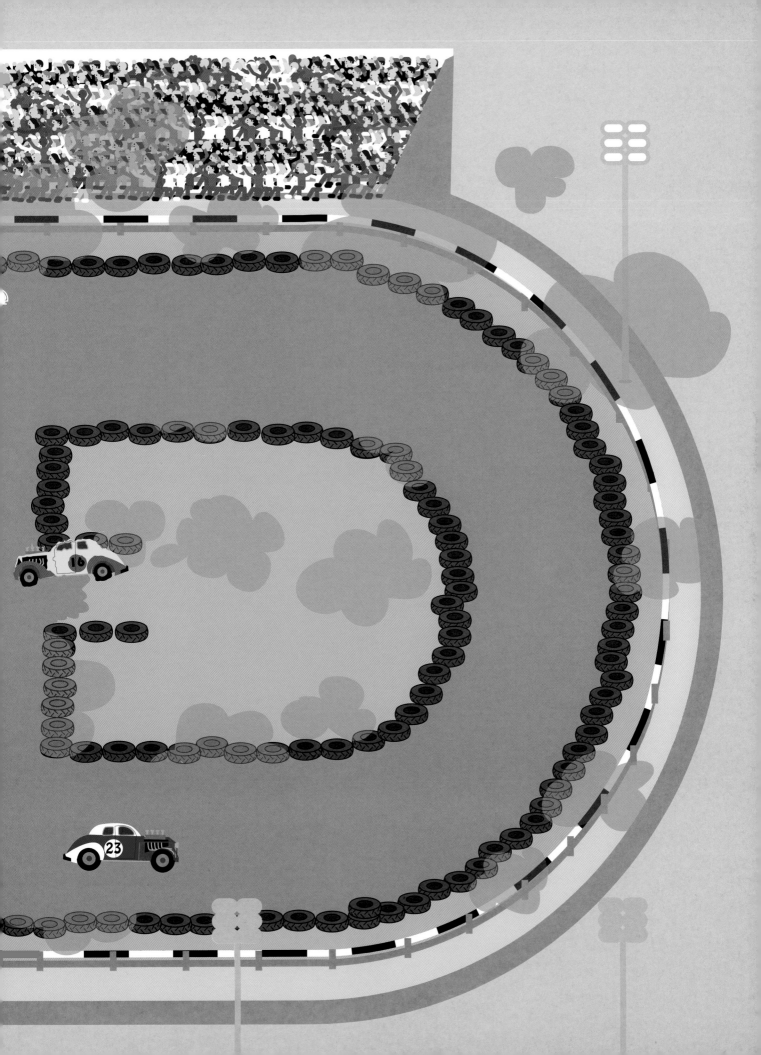

Pedal power

The country roads snake around the hillside.
Fill them with cyclists pedaling hard to win the race.

Back in time

This museum is home to vehicles from the past. Fill it with stickers of early flying machines and old-fashioned transportation.

Houseboat vacation

Every summer, the river is full of brightly-colored boats. Use the decorated houseboat stickers to brighten up this happy river scene.

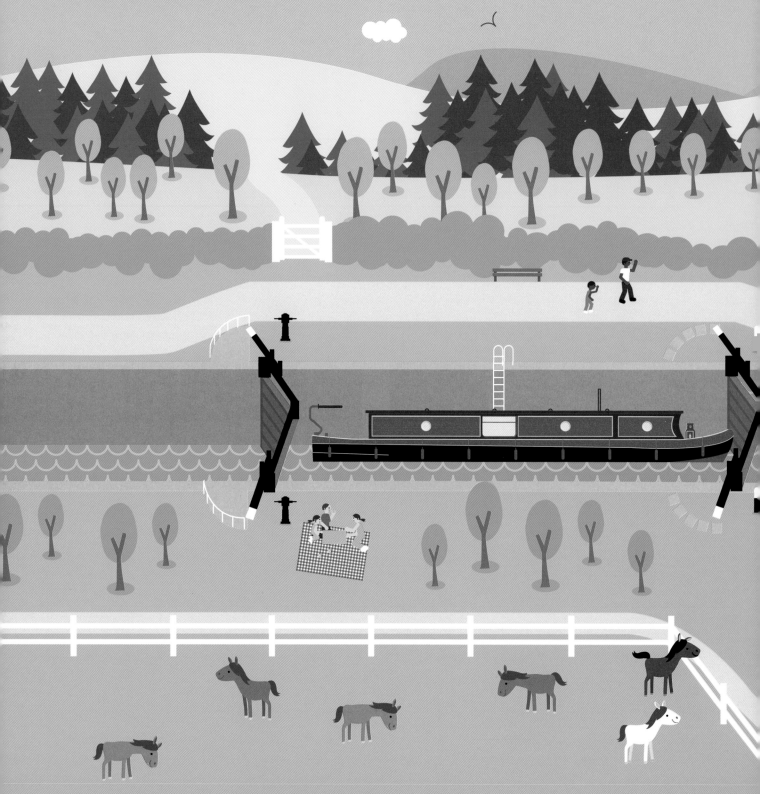

Fantasy future

How will we travel in the future? Fill this fantasy scene with futuristic vehicle stickers and imagine what it might be like to live there.